Dennis the Menace Rides Again

by Hank Ketcham

New York
Henry Holt and Company

The author is grateful to the Post-Hall Syndicate, Inc., in whose columns these cartoons originally appeared.

Library of Congress Catalog Card Number: 55-10641

84902-0415
Printed in the United States of America

"I THOUGHT I'D COME AND MEET YOU, DAD, SO I COULD TELL YOU *MY* SIDE OF THE STORY."

"DON'T YOU REMEMBER? MOM SAID OPEN ALL THE WINDOWS IF HE LIGHTS ONE OF THOSE CHEAP CIGARS."

"IT'S NOT A REAL TATTOO, ALICE. IT COMES OFF WITH SOAP AND WATER."

"WAIT 'TIL SHE OPENS *MY* PRESENT. SHE DIDN'T BELIEVE ME WHEN I TOLD HER IT WAS NOTHIN'."

"DEAR, WILL YOU LOOK AND SEE IF THERE ARE A
COUPLE OF FROGS IN YOUR BRIEFCASE?"

*WHY *CAN'T* HE SEE IT? IT'S A DOG MOVIE, ISN'T IT? HE'S A *DOG*, ISN'T HE?*

"THAT'S BATHROOM WATER . . . . I WANTED *KITCHEN* WATER!"

"THINK, MARTHA, *THINK!* IF WE DON'T FIND A BABY SITTER FOR THE MITCHELLS, THEY'LL BRING HIM OVER HERE!"

"I DON'T WANNA GO ANYWHERE I CAN'T RIDE A HORSE!"

"I'LL BET YOU'LL BE GLAD TO GET HOME AND PUT ON YOUR OLD CLOTHES, TOO!"

"YOU'D THINK THERE WASN'T ANOTHER DRUM IN TOWN! HALF THE PEOPLE ON THIS STREET WANT TO BUY *MINE!*"

"OKAY IF I LOOK AT YOUR FUNNY PAPER, MISTER?"

"IT'S JUST A CATERPILLAR, BUT DON'T TELL NOBODY."

"HI, MOM! IS THAT DAD?"

"LOOK AROUND, YOUNG MAN. I'M SUPPOSED TO HAVE ANOTHER BANANA!"

"I LOST MY APPETITE IN MRS. WILSON'S KITCHEN."

"HEY, MOM! MRS. GERBER'S CARDS ALL LOOK LIKE LITTLE *VALENTINES!*"

"WE COULD GO DOWN TO THE CANDY STORE IF YOU'D ASK
YOUR PRETTY MOTHER FOR A DIME."

"WILL YOU PLEASE PIPE DOWN? I DON'T *WANT* YOU TO HOLD MY GLASSES!"

"*I* SAY IT'S ALL YOU CAN DRINK. *THAT'S* WHO SAYS IT'S ALL YOU CAN DRINK!"

"CAN RUFF INVITE A FRIEND FOR SUPPER?"

"I LIKE TELEVISION BETTER. IT'S NOT SO FAR TO THE BATHROOM."

"HEY, WAKE UP! YOUR ICE CREAM'S RUNNIN' DOWN YOUR ARM!"

"DID YOU KNOW THE PAINT'S COMIN' OFF ONE OF THE LITTLE PIGS THAT STAYED HOME?"

"Gee, you act like you never *FELT* an icicle before."

"WHAT A SWELL PARTY! MRS. TAYLOR DROPPED THE CAKE
AND MOST OF THE GIRLS WOULDN'T EAT ANY!"

"I'M JUST GARGLING. WHO SAID I WAS DROWNING IN THE BATHTUB?"

"WHY DO YOU CALL IT MY BEDROOM IF I CAN'T EVEN LOCK THE DOOR?"

"MAD, ISN'T SHE?"

"I THINK I'LL TURN ON THE TELEVISION. OKAY? HUH? OKAY
IF I TURN IT ON? DAD? MOM? OKAY?....."

"AND IF YOU HURT HER AGAIN, I'LL *KICK YOU AGAIN!*"

"I'M JUST A LITTLE KID. I'LL GET _SICK_ IF I DON'T EAT ANY LUNCH!"

"GEE, YOU'RE *LOTS* OF FUN! ARE YOU **SURE** YOU'RE A GIRL?"

"WAIT 'TIL YOU SEE HOW NEAT WE'VE BEEN STACKING THE DIRTY DISHES, MOM!"

"FOR GOSH SAKES! WHAT'S CUTE ABOUT TAKIN' A BATH?"

"I *TOLD* YOU WHY! I'M GONNA WATCH A COWBOY MOVIE AT NINE O'CLOCK, AND MY FOLKS SEND ME TO BED AT EIGHT."

"MAYBE I'D BETTER SEE IF DAD'S GETTING ENOUGH AIR IN THAT CLOSET."

"DON'T WORRY. HE'LL MAKE A LOT OF NOISE, BUT HE'S TOO OLD TO CLIMB UP HERE."

" YOU LOOK HUNGRY. WHY DON'T YOU ASK YOUR MOM FOR TWO PEANUT BUTTER SANDWICHES? "

"I ALREADY TRIED TO HELP MOM, BUT SHE SENT ME OUT TO HELP YOU."

"WHAT ARE YOU *WAITIN'* FOR, DAD? *AFRAID?*"

"WHY DIDN'T YOU COME OUT? YOU NEVER **SAW** SO MANY PLANES!"

"YOU KNOW THAT BIG PICTURE WINDOW THE WILSONS USED TO HAVE?"

" MY FOLKS ARE GETTING TO THE AGE NOW WHERE THEY EXPECT ME TO HANG MY CLOTHES UP. "

"WELL, WE TOOK HIM FOR A CANOE RIDE. ANY MORE BRIGHT IDEAS?"

"WELL? *NOW* ARE YOU READY TO SAY YOU'RE SORRY?"

"AND I CAN'T FIND MY MOTHER, EITHER!"

"*MY* SPOON ISN'T GREASY!"

"HEY, DID YOU FORGET YOU LEFT ME UPSTAIRS SOAKING?"

"SEE? ONCE THEY'RE DEAD,
THEY'RE *DEAD!*"

"YES, I CAN SEE THE BALL. ANYMORE QUESTIONS?"

"YOU WERE RIGHT, MOM! HER BEDS AREN'T MADE!"

"THAT WAS JUST FOR LAUGHS, DAD. I'LL TURN IT ON SLOW THIS TIME."

"AM I GONNA PICK UP MY TOYS? YOU MEAN I HAVE A CHOICE?"

"WOULD IT HURT ANYTHING IF I LEFT THE WATER RUNNING IN THE BATHROOM?"

"I'M ALL RIGHT, SO DON'T SNEAK UP ON ME WITH ANY NOSE DROPS!"

"*WAKE UP, DAD!*"

"YOU WERE RIGHT, MOM. I'M TOO LITTLE TO USE GLUE."

"LISTEN, ALICE, HE'S JUST FAKING BECAUSE HE KNOWS
YOU'LL JUMP ON ME! ALICE, LISTEN A MINUTE . . ."

"BUT NOBODY'LL SEE ME UNTIL *TOMORROW!*"

"MY MOTHER ISN'T HOME, BUT I'LL ASK MY DAD IF YOU CAN COME IN. HE'S RIGHT HERE BEHIND THE DOOR."

"... AN' BLOW WHISTLES AN' HORNS AN' RING BELLS AN' SING SONGS AN' YELL 'HAPPY NEW YEAR'...AND THEN THEY WANTA KNOW HOW COME I'M NOT SLEEPIN'!"